Maximizing Your Enneagram Type

A WORKBOOK

Maximizing Your Enneagram Type

A WORKBOOK

Improve your Life
by Identifying, Understanding,
and Developing your Strengths.

John Carlini, D.Min.

Center of Growth Publications
Highwood, IL 60040

Cover design and typesetting: Ambush Graphics

ISBN: 978-0-69230551-5

Center of Growth Publications
Highwood, IL 60040

www.centerofgrowth.com

Contents

Introduction

This workbook is designed to be used with Jerome Wagner's book, *The Enneagram Spectrum of Personality Styles*, and his Enneagram test (WEPSS). Both resources are described in Chapter 1. This workbook is intended for people who have not yet taken the Enneagram, people who have taken the Enneagram test and have a basic knowledge of the Enneagram, and people who are extremely conversant in the Enneagram. As a Spiritual Director, this workbook can be used as a tool for directees to identify and bring issues to the direction time. Counselors can use this with their clients to help them understand themselves and formulate plans of action.

This guide grew out of my own experience with the Enneagram. Instructors and mentors suggested that reading about the Enneagram and attending Enneagram seminars would provide good experiences for me to grow in competence as a spiritual director. I learned a great deal and gained a lot of insight into how I think, act, speak, and make decisions. When present with others who have taken the Enneagram, we could discuss, with ease, our numbers and describe ourselves based on our Enneagram Style. This was rewarding and gave me an insight into others and myself that I may not have otherwise gained.

However, that didn't seem to satisfy me. Just naming the patterns and being able to identify them as resourceful or non-resourceful left me longing for more. In many ways, I'm a pragmatist so when I tell myself I have a lot of knowledge concerning the Enneagram, my immediate response is, "So what? What can you do with that?" Sure, understanding Enneagram styles helps us understand one another, but I have a desire to take this knowledge and apply it to my spiritual growth. I want to use the Enneagram as a way in which I can continue to grow as a person every day.

Therefore, I devised a way I could personally take these insights I had learned about myself and use them as a tool for personal and spiritual growth. In the interest of self-disclosure, I am an Evangelical Covenant Church pastor and spiritual director. I have tried to offer this workbook in a non-sectarian way. However, my point of reference is Christianity and I have used examples from the Christian tradition from time-to-time and identified unique Christian resources. Since I am not an expert on comparative religions, I encourage you to substitute your own language and traditions to the spiritual nature of some of the exercises. Feel free to approach these portions with your own brand of spirituality.

I started this work from a couple of philosophical assumptions. First of all, even though we may be a particular number on the Enneagram; growing as a person comes as we can incorporate the best from all the styles. In fact, as we look at the core value of each style, we can easily see that we aspire to all of them; goodness, love, competency, originality, wisdom, loyalty, joy, power, and peace. Mature, well-rounded individuals allow these qualities to manifest themselves in their lives on a regular basis. Therefore, once we start our work through the Enneagram, we are on a lifelong pursuit to integrate all the resourceful qualities into our lives. Second, I set up the workbook in a way that gets us to explore, develop, and build on our strengths. From there, we can start to identify our deficiencies and then use our strengths and resources to overcome them. Third, my hope is that we all have a spiritual director, counselor, mentor, or a wise friend with whom we can bounce ideas around. We often overlook people as valuable resources. If you're anything like me, you can easily fool yourself and justify just about any thoughts, words, or behaviors. It is helpful to have someone to tell you if you are on the right track or full of beans. Therefore, we will bring to bear all our strengths and resources on our weaknesses in the hope of living less out of our weaknesses and more out of our strengths. It is also possible for us to turn some of our weaknesses into strengths. This enables us to grow into more well-rounded individuals.

I have designed the workbook for the rhythm of doing one chapter per month. To do a chapter just to get it done defeats the purpose of the workbook. The workbook is designed in a way so that you may take your time pondering your answers and solidifying your strengths in order for them to become second nature to you. If it takes you more than a month to fully ingest the chapter, that's okay; take all the time you need. Don't go on to the next chapter until you feel as if you have savored every last morsel of truth for yourself. Further, most people meet with their spiritual director once a month. To me, this seems to be the guideline for a good rhythm. But, you should find a rhythm that works for you.

My hope is that you will continue to grow throughout your whole life; right up until the day you pass into the next world. So, in answer to the question, "When will I be done?" I will quote that great philosopher and theologian, Yogi Berra, "It ain't over 'til it's over."

Chapter 1

YOUR TOOL BOX FOR LIFE

Pre-Workbook Requirements

1. Go to www.WEPSS.com and take the Enneagram test.

2. Familiarize yourself with the Enneagram and with your particular number by reading *The Enneagram Spectrum of Personality Styles* by Jerome Wagner.

3. Go to www.enneagraminstitute.com and sign up for the free enneathought for the day. These daily thoughts are not only fun; they are insightful and will help you understand your type better as you proceed through this workbook.

Write your name and address on the left side of the space below.

In the right side of the space above, write your name and address with your other hand.

Make some observations about the exercise. What did you notice about comparing the two? How did you feel in each instance?

I felt uncomfortable writing with my left hand.

Think about the following:

- Even though the second writing looks worse than the first, you can most likely still read both of them. √

- Even though you felt awkward during the time you wrote with your non-dominate hand, you were still able to accomplish it.√

- Being who you are is not an excuse for what you do. We can choose to change and become more resourceful people. We are not stuck or labeled by our Enneagram style. √

A view towards these exercises:

I view each number on the Enneagram as a tool box. All the resourceful traits you inherit as part of that number should be viewed as tools you can use as you go through different life situations.

The goal is to maximize those tools you already have while at the same time developing potential tools listed as non-resourceful.

We have all nine tool boxes available to us. We may be clumsy as we start to use them, but just like writing with our non-dominate hands, with practice, we can use and develop them. The more tools we have at our disposal at any given time, gives us more options to embrace what stands before us; whether enjoying something pleasant or successfully navigating through something difficult.

Read the chapter in Wagner's *The Enneagram Spectrum* that corresponds to your style. Go to the positive descriptors of your particular number and write down only those characteristics that describe you. Add to that list any other things that positively describe you.

To give you an idea of how to answer the questions, I will write one or two responses. Since I am type 9, I took responses from a group of 9s. I will always use the first person "I" in each of the prompted responses because I want you to make each answer personal. You should put as many qualities that apply to you even though I will just give one or two answers. The more complete your answers; the more insight you will gain.

I am: Diplomatic, Low Key, Settled, Peaceful, etc.

I am ambitious, adaptable efficient, doer, and goal-oriented, motivator, enthusiastic, popular, dynamic, competent

Take time to read over this list. Read these qualities over again and remember these are tools you already possess. These are tools you bring to all sorts of relationships: personal, work, social, religious, etc. This is what you have to offer. Take time to write about who you are and what you bring to the table

I am pleasant to be around and I am a happy person.

I am a dedicated and loyal worker.
I am devoted to my industry & career.
I am fiercely intelligent.
I am very attractive
I am a warrior.
I am a devilish, gold-hearted rebel.
I am rugged. I am a driving force.

How do you use these tools...

...at work?

When my work is done,
I look to help others with their work.

...in family relationships?

> *I like to bring a sense of humor to my family
> and try to mediate conflicts.*

...in other relationships?

> *I am a great team player and I'm a hard worker.*

...in a relationship with God?

I'm thankful, I don't complain, and I'm content.

Look over your tools again. List the 4 words you feel the most comfortable with. These will be your primary "go to" behaviors. A further fun exercise is to go back and look at all the tools you listed and see how they fall under each of these words and form clusters.

The 4 words that describe me are, peaceful,
content, team player, sense of humor.

REFLECTIONS

1. What have I learned new about myself?

2. What do I like about what I've learned about myself?

3. What do I need to revisit and/or follow up on?

4. What can I bring to my spiritual director or counselor
for further discussion?

Chapter 2

YOUR WINGMAN/WOMAN

Having a good handle on our wing style can give us some real help and insight into how we act under normal conditions. In the dating world, it's always good to have a good wingman/woman around. The wingman's/woman's role is to support his or her friend's needs as he/she approaches potential partners. The wingman provides emotional support and is supposed to make his friend look good to the potential partner. He is also there to help avoid undesirable suitors and protect us from making dangerous choices; perhaps he will take our car keys if we have had too much to drink. The better the wingman/woman knows his/her friend, the more effective he/she will be.

With our enneatype comes a wingman/woman as well. Our wing helps our type to be the best it can be. It complements our basic style. It informs and influences the way we use our basic style.

The numbers that stand on either side of your enneatype are your potential wing. What are the numbers on each side of your enneatype? Write them down along with the percentile score they received on the test.

8 = 52

1 = 98.7

The highest one is typically your wing although we often exhibit character-istics from the weaker wing also. Write down the title given to your wing style. (You can find this on page 37 of Wagner's book and at the beginning of each chapter that describes each style.)

1 = The Good Person

Now, look at the description of your wing. Go through the list of positive descriptors, writing down only those that describe you.

Responsible, dedicated, conscientious, etc.

How would you describe your wingman/woman (your Enneagram wing)?

My wingman knows what the rules are
and what is right and wrong.

Go back to Chapter One in this workbook and read the way you described yourself as a person. Reread how you positively use your tools at work and in different relationships. How does your wing influence where you focus your gifts?

It helps me to be a good husband,
good father, and a good friend.

Now go back to the chapter in Wagner's book that describes your primary style. Write down the following:

Distorting Paradigm: *Resignation (giving up)*

Passion: *Laziness*

Defense Mechanism: *Narcotization*

Area of Avoidance: *Conflict*

Take some time to think about these traits and how they can be a hindrance to your everyday life. Can you see how these can cause you to make some poor choices? Write your thoughts about these.

> *I can easily give up and simply go along to get along.*

How can your wingman/woman help you overcome these?

> *My wing informs me that there are a set of values*
> *beyond those of the utilitarian. If what I am thinking is*
> *the best course of action to take, I need to take it;*
> *even if it causes conflict.*

Now go back to the chapter in Wagner's book that describes your primary style. Write down the following:

The title of that style: **The peaceful person**

The objective paradigm: **Love**

The virtue: **Action**

Take some time to think about how these can make you a better person who can embrace life with peace, joy, and contentment. How can these help you achieve your goals while at the same time becoming a better human being? Christians may phrase this as becoming more like Christ.

I need to keep fully engaged with what I'm doing in order to get the best result possible. I need to address them honestly even though it may cause conflict.

How can your wingman/woman keep your attention directed towards these goals?

My wing can keep me focused on what is true and what is right.

As you go through the workbook, keep in mind that your wing informs and influences the choices you make and the tools you use. Our wing can keep our attention focused on the high side of our primary styles. They can also keep us from acting out on the low side of our personality.

REFLECTIONS

1. What have I learned new about myself?

2. What do I like about what I've learned about myself?

3. What do I need to revisit and/or follow up on?

4. What can I bring to my spiritual director or counselor
for further discussion?

Chapter 3

"Q" BRANCH

The outcome of many wars throughout history has been determined by how successful or unsuccessful the Quartermaster Branch has been at getting the proper supplies and ammunition to the troops fighting the battles on the front lines.

In the James Bond movies, there is a character named "Q" who works at supplying James Bond with all the proper tools needed to complete the mission. His job is to make sure the agents are equipped with the proper transportation, communications, and weapons.

A typical James Bond scene would be to encounter Bond on a serene ride through the countryside, when all of a sudden...an oncoming car steers in his lane and heads directly towards him. In his rearview mirror, he sees a motorcycle speeding up while firing a machine gun. And to make things worse, a helicopter looms overhead. For a moment, fear wakes him up; but then he pushes a button, a rocket fires from his backseat, and the helicopter is blown up. He presses another button and giant tacks are laid down all across the road, the motorcycle's tires are punctured, and the rider is thrown off the motorcycle and over the cliff. There remains one more threat to deal with: the oncoming car. Bond presses a button and oil is laid down all over the road. Just at the last minute, he turns a knob, wings sprout from his car, the car takes off in the air, while the threatening car hits the oil spot and spins wildly out of control off the cliff. "Q" has saved Bond's life once again.

Note, "Q" is really gender neutral. Women fulfill these roles as well as men; in some cases, even better than men. Let's take everyday life, for example. A child playing on the playground falls off the slide and skins his knee. Immediately, one mother has an antiseptic spray to sanitize the wound, and another pulls a band aid out of her purse to cover it. I have seen women pull out needle and thread to sew buttons on their children's shirts in public; or safety pins to pin their husband's broken pants fasteners. Whether it is nail polish, cream, pins, ointments, and yes, even money; if an emergency arises away from home, the chances are that a woman has the solution in her purse. "Q" branch is invaluable to the success of any mission.

You may be interested to know that our personality tool box comes equipped with some of "Q's" tools. In Wagner's book, *The Enneagram Spectrum of Personality Styles*, under the chapter that describes your personality style, locate the section **Paradigm Shifts You May Experience Under Stressful Conditions.** For now, skip the sections titled *A Shift to the Low Side of Your Own Style* and *A Shift to the Low Side of Style* _____ *(there will be a particular number here).*

The style I go to when I'm under stress is **6** _____ (write the number here).

Find the chapter in Wagner's book that describes that particular style. Under the section that says, "Positive Descriptors of Your Style," list those descriptors that accurately describe you.

6 = Cautious, Reliable, Traditional, God-fearing, etc.

Take some time to read and reread these. Meditate on this and remember these are tools you can use when things get tough and you find yourself stressed.

Now, read the section (in the chapter on your primary style) that says *A Shift to the High Side of Style* __6____.

Take time to write these down. They are resources available to you under stressful situations. Make it personal; substitute "I" for "You". For example, when it says, "You can…" write "I can…" Replace all the third person pronouns with first person pronouns. Be sure to put these in words that are meaningful to you. You should be able to see the tools you have written above reflected in these statements.

I can find in myself the courage to be somebody and take a stand and state my case.

Now, it's time for you to describe some of the tools in your tool box that you can use when you find yourself under stress. Take some time and write out personal statements of how you can successfully navigate through difficult situations using the tools in your tool box.

I will be careful not to become lazy or resigned.
I will use my head to realistically assess the situation,
make a plan to see my way through,
and work hard to execute the plan.

Norman Wright (Christian counselor and author) once told me, "Repeat things for 30 days, and they will become part of your vocabulary." For 30 days, read through all the tools you listed in this chapter. Especially take time to read, speak aloud, and meditate on the personal statements you wrote in the last section. In times of distress, you will be able to pull these tools out as easily as James Bond knows what button to push and when to push it.

REFLECTIONS

1. What have I learned new about myself?

2. What do I like about what I've learned about myself?

3. What do I need to revisit and/or follow up on?

4. What can I bring to my spiritual director or counselor
for further discussion?

Chapter 4

KICKIN' IT

Have you ever been on a tropical beach with someone you really like and with a cool drink at your side? Imagine it! Lying in a hammock, just gazing out at the ocean while listening to the waves breaking on the shore. You sit up to take a sip of your cool drink, lie back in the hammock, and then again turn your silent attention towards the ocean.

That is the situation in which I find myself the most relaxed. I will be back in Playa Del Carmen next month. Unfortunately, I can only get to this spot two or three times a year.

Where is the place you feel the most relaxed? How often are you able to get there? Take some time to close your eyes and think about it. What are some of the things you hear, see, and smell? What kinds of feelings well up in you?

The sand, the salt in the air, the warm ocean, the warmth of the sun, and the company of my wife are some of the things I am feeling and experiencing. My mind Is free and clear. I am rested physically, emotionally, and spiritually. I feel free.

more space provided next page

We have seen that we have a dominant style in which we approach every-day life and we have a style we exhibit under stressful conditions. We also have a style we move to under relaxed conditions. Go to Wagner's book and find the chapter that describes your primary style. In the chapter, find the section labeled "Paradigm Shifts You May Experience Under Relaxed Conditions" and read that entire section.

Write out the statements that accurately describe you under "A Shift to the High Side of Your Own Style." Like before, make it personal. Substitute first person pronouns for second person. For example, change "You" to "I" and "your" to "mine."

I can focus. I am prompt. I get things done.
I'm starting to voice my own opinion.

Now, let's look at where you go when you are relaxed. In the very next section, "A Shift to the High Side of Style #, read only that section and list the high side characteristics. Write out the statements that apply to you, again making them personal.

*3 = I am focused and goal oriented. I can determine
what I want and make a plan to get it.*

Take the style you shift to under relaxed conditions and go to the chapter in Wagner's book that describes that style in full. Look at the list of positive descriptors that describe you.

Efficient, Get things done, Enthusiastic, Pragmatic, etc.

It seems as if we expend a lot of our energies dealing with and solving problems in our work-a-day-world. It's not often that we find ourselves in a relaxed enough state to embrace the gifts we have. In the Judeo-Christian tradition, God built a rhythm into life called Sabbath. Sabbath is a day in which people are not to work; but to rest mind, body, and soul. It is truly a time to relax.

Set about four hours aside to be alone, quiet, and relaxed. Read over all the answers you wrote down. Ponder them. When relaxed situations present themselves; these attitudes, behaviors, and habits are available to you. Many of them are natural to you. Others you need to think about. What do you like about yourself when you exhibit these qualities? Take some time to write out how you would like to incorporate these during the course of your everyday life; even if nothing special is going on or you are experiencing stressful situations.

I like knowing that people think of me as reliable and dependable. I like thinking that I am non-judgmental and that I am able to empathize. When I make decisions, they are pretty fair. I like knowing that I get things done.

Jews and Christians can regularly reflect on these if they consistently practice Sabbath. Solitude, silence, and retreats are other disciplines that foster these kinds of opportunities for growth. Others should set regular times aside to remind themselves of these qualities.

REFLECTIONS

1. What have I learned new about myself?

2. What do I like about what I've learned about myself?

3. What do I need to revisit and/or follow up on?

4. What can I bring to my spiritual director or counselor
for further discussion?

Chapter 5

LAYING OUT YOUR TREASURES

Our family vacations are interesting in so many ways. However, one thing that's constant is my wife and our son's insatiable appetites to search for and buy trinkets. Whether we are in the side streets of Venice, night markets in Asia, tent markets in Mexico, or flea markets in Florida; our daughter and I are constantly amazed at their energy to explore every booth. Sometimes, just to make sure they have not missed anything, they will go back through the market one more time. That's not the best part of the story. Our daughter's and my entertainment starts at the end of the day. Our son and my wife will carefully take out all the treasures they acquired that day, add to them all the treasures they bought the previous days on the vacation, and lay them out on the bed. They will look at them, admire them, and oftentimes count them. This ritual takes place at the end of each day while we are on vacation.

At this point, I would like you to take out all the treasures you have discovered about yourself, lay them out, look at them, and remember them. In fact, as you go through the portion of the book that follows, take them out often and remember to use them.

Before we move on, review your answers in the workbook Chapters 1-4.

How would you summarize your positive qualities:

In normal times (Chapter 1)?

> *I am a happy person who is a good team player.*
> *I'm easy to get along with, etc.*

As your wing influences you (Chapter 2)?

> *In general, I follow the rules and follow directions.*

In times of stress (Chapter 3)?

> *I am loyal, can formulate a plan, and stick to the plan.*
> *I don't give up easily.*

Under relaxed conditions (Chapter 4)?

> *I am thoughtful. I can think deeply, both philosophically*
> *and theologically. I am able to do honest self-reflection.*

Now, let's take a look at qualities that characterize our personality types.

Locate Figure 1 in Wagner's book (page 7.) Look at the Authentic Values. They are located in the very center circle. Take some time to write down all nine of them.

Now go back and circle; 1) Your primary type; 2) Your wing; 3) Your type under stress; and 4) Your type during relaxed conditions.

Those are qualities that belong specifically to your type. However, if you think about it, all of these are qualities to which we all aspire. An example from the Christian tradition. In his letter to the church in Galatia, the Apostle Paul said:

> [22] *But the fruit of the Spirit is love, joy, peace, patience,*
>   *kindness, goodness, faithfulness,*
> [23] *gentleness and self-control…*
> —*Galatians 5:22-23(TNIV)*

New Testament Bible commentators point out that the subject "fruit" is singular as is the verb "is." The twist comes in the predicate, which lists nine separate nouns. In normal parlance, we would say, "The fruits of the Spirit are," and then go on to name the nine fruits. Since Paul was a highly educated scholar, we have to assume that he did not make a simple grammatical error; that his usage here was intentional.

His intention is this. Since God the Holy Spirit takes up residence in each believer, the believer ought to start manifesting these named characteristics that belong to God and that He shares with His people. All of these qualities should start showing themselves in the believer's life. For example, it would be a mistake to think that we can be kind and patient; while not being gentle, loving, and joyful. This fruit comes as a package deal.

There are two points to consider in regards to the Enneagram. First of all, there are nine types in the Enneagram and there are nine fruits listed. In some ways, they are similar. Secondly, just as believers are expected to manifest the whole fruit; love, joy, peace, patience, kindness, goodness, gentleness, faithfulness, and self control; so will it be a good life-long process to exhibit all the Authentic Values of the other types as well as our own. Take some time to review them now and from time to time.

Describe what it would be like to have a best friend who exhibited all these qualities. Write down some specifics as well.

He would accept me for who I am, not what I could be.
I would never feel judged or shamed around her, etc.

Is that the type of person and friend you aspire to become? Isn't that really the goal of working through the Enneagram?

Yes and Yes

In the spirit of St. Francis', "Make me an instrument of Your peace," let's make this personal. Write down as an introductory statement, "Lord, make me an instrument of" or "I aspire to be a person of" and then write the Nine values of the Enneagram types.

Lord, make me an instrument of Peace.

Lord, make me an instrument of Goodness, etc.

So, if you choose to make that commitment, know that we have a long journey ahead. Our goal will be to correct false narratives, replace them with correct narratives, and try to add some more positive tools to our toolbox.

Go to the chapter on your particular type in Wagner's book. Locate the section titled "Positive Core Value Tendencies." Did you catch the wording there? It means that whether dormant or active, these core values are part of who we are in this particular type. Take time to read them, write them out, and read them once again. Please make the statements personal; instead of you, substitute I.

I value peace which is the tranquility of order.

*I have an intuitive sense and
appreciation for harmony.*

Doesn't that sound great? Do these appeal to you at a deeper level? The good news is that you already have many of the qualities and the others may simply be dormant. This is what we are aspiring to be. Since the rest of the book may be painful and some things will be difficult for us to acknowledge or own in our personality, please don't forget the tools you already have. Our goal is to use these tools to discover, develop, and integrate new tools. Also, if you are ready to courageously look at your flaws, please write a statement that you are willing to do so.

I know there are plenty of defective ways in which
I interact with God, with others, and myself. I am
committed to uncovering them and transforming them
into useful ways of being in the world.

REFLECTIONS

1. What have I learned new about myself?

2. What do I like about what I've learned about myself?

3. What do I need to revisit and/or follow up on?

4. What can I bring to my spiritual director or counselor
for further discussion?

Chapter 6

WHO'S IN THE DRIVER'S SEAT?

In the *Phaedrus*, Plato describes the soul as two horses pulling a chariot with a charioteer. Plato divided the soul into three parts; the rational, the spirited, and the appetitive. The charioteer represented the rational part of the soul, and the two horses represented the spirited and the appetitive.

For Plato, the appetitive part of our soul represents all our desires; to eat, to drink, to have sex, etc. The spirited portion represents courage and energy. The rational portion oversees both horses and keeps them focused and on track. It would be disastrous for Plato if the spirited portion or the appetitive portion took over the reins and started to drive the chariot.

Interestingly enough, the Enneagram has three centers that correspond to Plato's analogy; the heart, the head, and the gut. In general, styles 2, 3, and 4, tend to be driven by the heart. Styles 5, 6, and 7 tend to have their head in the driver's seat. Styles 8, 9, and 1, tend to have their gut in the driver's seat.

What is your style? __9__

What is your center? <u>Gut</u>

Read the section "Three Centers or Instincts" (pages 30-36) in Wagner's book. Look at the diagram on page 32. Read the description of your particular center and summarize your center. Add some of your own personal thoughts about your particular center.

I often make decisions based on fear of conflict and fear of being inadequate. I often make decisions based on my gut feeling.

At this point, we must tinker with Plato's analogy. Like Plato's analogy, we need to rely on all three centers. Making a decision without accessing all three centers will result in bad decisions. If your center is the head, and you refuse to access the heart and the gut, you may leave a string of hurt people in your wake. If you are a gut person and don't use your head or your heart, you can find yourself in a lot of trouble. Again, people who make decisions based solely on their heart also end up making bad decisions.

Here is where we may want to differ from Plato. If we work hard and develop all centers, we can allow one of the other centers to drive. There are occasions when it would be best to let the heart drive. At other times, it may be better to let the gut drive. And in other situations, it may be better if we let the head take the wheel. This takes courage and humility.

Speaking from a Christian perspective, when we fail to use all our centers, we can end up hurting a lot of people, we hurt God, and we hurt ourselves. We call that sin.

And that brings us to the vice of each style. Just as each style comes with certain tools; each style comes with a particular weakness.

Heart	Head	Gut
2 – Pride	5 – Stinginess	8 – Lust
3 – Deceit	6 – Fear	9 – Indolence (Sloth)
4 – Envy	7 – Gluttony	1 – Anger

Wagner identifies these vices as maladaptive schema in his chart on page 23.

What is your weakness/temptation/vice?

Indolence (Sloth)

In Wagner's book, go back to the chapter that describes your primary style. Locate the section titled "Passion:(Your Particular vice)" Read it and write down what you think this vice means.

> *Laziness for me is not just being lazy. It is a resignation; an attitude that means I don't care. I often detach from people and events that seem to be too much trouble. I can neglect important things; even myself.*

Go to the chapter that describes the style of your wing. What is the passion/weakness there? Describe this vice.

*Anger – Sometimes I respond in anger when I'm afraid
or feel threatened.*

Go to the chapter that describes your style under stress. Do the same analysis you did above with the passion. Be as specific as you can.

*6=Fear – Sometimes I will just run away. Sometimes I
engage in risky behavior.*

Go to the chapter that describes your style under relaxed conditions and again do the same kind of analysis. Be as specific as you can.

> *3=Deceit – Many of my sins are directly related to when I'm trying to look smart, to look holy, and to look good. I try to fit in by going along on the surface. I often hide my feelings.*

What's the hook? What draws us into these undesirable behaviors? Turn to page 7 in Wagner's book. Level II identifies our Areas of Avoidance. Then go to the chapter on your particular style and read the two sections; "Virtue" and "Passion." In other words, we come with a built-in fear that drives our vice. What is the fear listed in the chart for your particular style? It's also worth listing the fear of your wing, your style under stress, and your style under relaxed conditions. Also read the corresponding section called "Area of Avoidance" in each chapter that applies to your particular style.

Conflict – Anger – Deviance - Failure

Take some time to meditate on these. Can you see how these things cause your fear? How do you tend to avoid these things? Don't short cut this step. It's important to know what kinds of things draw us into less resourceful attitudes and behaviors. You need to be brutally honest with yourself at this stage. Describe how your vices cover up your fears and help you avoid things you need to address. You can be both general and specific in these observations.

A lot of my energy is spent on avoiding conflict. If something bad happens, I become slothful in the sense that I say, "I don't care." I can easily avoid stressful situations. I can make decisions based on what is the easiest course of action that helps me to avoid the conflict.

The three underlying attitudes that cause my sin are:
Lust for pride, lust for food, fear. I can waste time
watching television or eating food.

Back on page 7 of Wagner's book; look at Level III and write down your defense mechanisms. Again, look to your primary style, your wing, your relaxed style, and your stressed style. Write them down; read the section labeled "Defense Mechanism" under your style chapter, and meditate on how they help you avoid addressing those things of which you are afraid.

9 – Narcotization – I overeat regularly and watch
television for hours

1 – Reaction Formation – I deny when I'm angry or hurt.
I just say, "I'm okay."

3 – Identification – I try to put on a good face and
pretend I'm competent.

6 – Projection – I tend to notice others who pretend to
be smart and holy.

Don't go on until you can identify some of the people and situations that move you towards less resourceful behavior. Describe how you non-resourcefully deal with these. It's important to understand exactly how we end up shooting ourselves in the foot. Do you think, at this point, you can identify some of your weaknesses?

Argumentative people
Having to confront people

Let's take a test. As we said earlier, we ought to strive to allow all the virtues to manifest themselves in our lives while we learn to move away from the vices. All the virtues are available to us and, likewise, all of the vices can tempt and capture us. Mark on the continuum where you think you are.

VICE	VIRTUE
Lust--	Innocence
Sloth---	Action
Anger--	Serenity
Pride---	Humility
Deceit ---	Truthfulness
Envy --	Equanimity
Greed-------------------------- ---	Detachment
Fear--	Courage
Gluttony--	Sobriety

It's important to note; these are not specific behaviors. These are attitudes that drive our behaviors. We are always somewhere on the continuum. Our goal is to try and keep moving towards the virtues.

Depending on when we take this test, we will find ourselves at different places on the continuum. What we want to do is notice our trends as time go on. This is not meant to be an absolute diagnostic tool. It is meant for us to use regularly to detect trends and movements as we mature

At this point, we are not trying to "fix" anything. This has been an exercise to see what's in the driver's seat. Make some observations about what you have learned so far.

I can see that I'm not completely vice or virtue. I am always moving somewhere along the continuum.

I'm able to identify my hooks and I think I am being more intentional to embrace situations with a goal of moving towards the virtues.

REFLECTIONS

1. What have I learned new about myself?

2. What do I like about what I've learned about myself?

3. What do I need to revisit and/or follow up on?

4. What can I bring to my spiritual director or counselor
for further discussion?

Chapter 7

BECOMING A PROFILER

We have all seen television programs or movies where the police analyze a crime or a series of crimes and try to figure out what kind of person could have committed them. They try to compile a profile of the person. They try to determine personality type, economic status, upbringing, triggers, and victim types. After determining a particular profile, the police can then concentrate on apprehending the criminal and prevent further crimes. It's hard work and time consuming but it often produces fruitful results.

Our goal in this chapter is to take a good, hard, and honest look at our thoughts, words, and behaviors in response to different situations in which we find ourselves. Profiling ourselves can result in making a roadmap for our future growth. Some of this will be a review of previous chapters so you ought to be becoming more familiar with your reactions.

Let's first profile our positive values, tendencies, and characteristics.

From page 7 in Wagner's book, find your genuine core value and write that down. You will find these core values in the most inner circle of the diagram.

9 = Peace

Go to the chapter describing your style and read through the section (column) that describes your Positive Core Value Tendencies. Write a positive profile for yourself. This has to do with what you want to bring to the world.

I want people to live together in peace.
It doesn't seem that hard to me if people choose
not to be selfish. It seems logical to me that everyone is
happier as they learn to live with each other.
This takes some putting away our egos and humbly
trying to understand each other. I'd like to be a person
who brings harmony. I'm generally forgiving and tolerant
of others and can't understand when others are not.

Now, turn to page 19 and write down your positive cognitive (intellectual) response to the world. It is found in the inner circle of this diagram.

9=Love

Again, turn to the chapter on your particular style and locate the paragraph describing your positive intellectual way of engaging the world. The paragraph is titled "Objective Paradigm." Summarize the potential you have to respond to situations.

When I see a need, I am a good worker. I can put my mind to things, embrace the reality of the situation, and work to make it better.

I feel loved by God and loved by others. I genuinely love others and want to journey with them through life.

Finally, turn to page 23 and list your positive emotional response to the world. It is found again in the inner circle.

9=Action

In the chapter that describes your particular style, locate the section labeled "Virtue." Read that paragraph and summarize it.

When I see people in need, I want to help.
I want to always be part of the solution. I am willing
to do what needs to be done.

At this point, write down the above responses together:

Your Fundamental Core Value is: *Peace*

Your Positive Intellectual Response is: *Love*

Your Positive Emotional Response is: *Action*

These are ways in which you can engage the people and circumstances that come your way. The more you can engage others like this, the more empowered they will feel. The more circumstances you encounter with these attitudes, values, and behaviors; the more you will be able to accomplish. This right thinking followed up by right behaviors will lead to good and peaceful feelings. In general, you will feel good about yourself.

Now, let's take a look at our negative profile. In other words, when we see these types of behaviors manifesting themselves, we can realize we are thinking, speaking, and behaving in non-resourceful ways that can harm others and make our situation worse. We worked in depth on these in the last chapter, so just go back and review your answers, think about them some more, and record your answers here.

On page 7 of Wagner's book, locate your primary area of avoidance. We also talked about this particular trait as our personal fear. Record that fear here and explain what these fears look like to you as you live your everyday life. Be as specific as you can.

Conflict – There are times when I feel people will not like me or they may abandon me if I disagree with them. Sometimes I may not express my personal thoughts or opinions if I know they disagree with someone else's.

I think I'm pretty selfish in this way. I don't want anyone or anything messing with my peace. I'm willing to sacrifice almost anything if I know someone likes me.

Let me make an observation at this point. In avoiding these fears, we actually carry ourselves away from our core. In most cases, in order to get back to our core authentic selves, we must actually journey back through these fears to get there. That's why we have to use the above positive tools to get us back to our authentic selves. It certainly is not a pleasant thought but that is the journey. Write down where your journey will have to take you.

In order for me to experience genuine peace, I will have to journey through conflict. I will need to learn to embrace conflict as a normal part of life and develop strategies that will enable me to deal with conflict in a healthy way.

Again, from page 7, write down your defense mechanism. Referring to this as negative, I refer to this as my "trick".

My trick is Narcotization.

In your particular style chapter, read Wagner's definition of these terms and try to personally define them for yourself.

Narcotization = To dull my feelings. I think my most frequent phrase is, "I don't care."

From the last chapter in this workbook, go back and look at how these play out in your thoughts, words, and behaviors. You had to take a look at your vices. These tend to be where we face the greatest temptations. For Jews and Christians, this is where we fight most of our spiritual battles. They tend to be our primary sins. In order to face our primary area of avoidance and fears, we have to ask, "How do these sins help us to deal with our fears?" You see, they have to work to some degree; otherwise we wouldn't be tempted to use them. Take some time to review this. Name them and write down how these maladaptive behaviors help us to avoid our fear. Also, relate them to your defense mechanism you named above. You can find these vices listed in the outer circle on page 23 in Wagner's book. In addition to this, to get a more complete understanding, find your negative intellectual response in the outer circle on page 19. Think of specific situations.

Narcotization / Sloth / Resignation – In being so afraid of conflict, I tend to minimize it. I can deny it affects me. I can give up and say it doesn't matter or I don't care. I refuse to examine how I'm hurt or how I'm affected. I can just eat or drink and not think about it.

Best example – I can mindlessly and endlessly watch television and stuff my face with food and drink.

In the Judeo Christian tradition, we could call this "worshiping idols." The thing about worshiping idols is although they bring some instant relief and gratification; they end up draining us of time, money, and energy. The frustrating thing is they don't bring lasting satisfaction. After expending our time, money, and energy, they leave us unfulfilled and hungry for more. How is this defective way of dealing with your area of avoidance or your fundamental fear robbing you?

I'm gaining weight. It affects my health and my mood negatively; high blood pressure, high cholesterol, no energy, moody, etc.

In order to gain some perspective on where you are, again mark the following charts. I'm going to contrast them by labeling the resourceful behavior as a virtue and the non-resourceful behavior as a vice. They seem to carry more emotional and intellectual weight with those titles. The idea is to identify which sense is motivating your present behavior. The focus is on your primary type; but feel free to examine yourself according to all the style numbers.

Emotional Responses to the World

VICE   **VIRTUE**

Lust-- Innocence

Sloth--Action

Anger--Serenity

Pride-- Humility

Deceit-- Truthfulness

Envy--- Equanimity

Greed--Detachment

Fear--- Courage

Gluttony--Sobriety

Cognitive/Intellectual Responses to the World

VICE	VIRTUE
Vindication	Justice
Resignation	Love
Perfection	Wholeness
Co-Dependence	Freedom
Efficiency	Hope
Specialness	Originality
Intellectualization	Understanding
Doubt/Dogma	Faith
Pleasure	Work

Authenticity

FEAR   **CORE SELF**

Weakness--Power

Conflict-- Peace

Anger-- Goodness

Needy ---Love

Failure --- Efficiency

Ordinariness -- Originality

Emptiness ---Wisdom

Deviance-- --------------------------- Loyalty

Pain -- Joy

Remember, this is so you can track trends as you go back and evaluate yourself. We will always be moving along the continuum. The intent is to identify which characteristic seems to be motivating you and to what level. The goal is that we continue to show a pattern of moving towards the positive side of the charts. We may take steps backwards from time to time but we hope the trend will be upwards.

Take time to find the section titled "What You Miss as a Result of the Distortion of Your Style" in the chapter that describes your style. Read it and write down what you could possibly be missing. Add your own thoughts as well.

Being loved simply for who I am; not what I do
A genuine sense of self-worth
Expressing my opinion when I could be right
Feeling that my opinion really matters

Presently, we have some idea of how we respond positively and negatively under normal everyday life situations. Let's now take a look at how we respond negatively under stress. Before going on, go back and review Chapter 3 in this workbook. Summarize all the tools you have to address stressful situations in a healthy manner.

I am disciplined and can get work done. I can focus and push through my fears. I can be loyal and I can focus on doing what is right.

I can use my head instead of my emotions. I can formulate plans and get organized.

In Wagner's book describing your particular style, locate the section "Paradigm Shifts You May Experience Under Stressful Conditions. Read the sections titled "A Shift to the Low Side of Your Own Style" and "A Shift to the Low Side of Style __6__." Write down all that apply to you.

What's the use? Resigned, Shut down / Avoid confrontation, Stubborn, etc.

If you want more information, find the chapter that is dedicated to the style number you go to under stress and read through the negative descriptors, and go through the negative portions of that particular style; area of avoidance, defense mechanism, vice, distorted core characteristics, distorting paradigm, and passion. Form a profile of how you could respond to stressful situations in a negative way. I'm sure you have noticed other destructive ways you handle stress. List those as well.

> *Under stress, I'm the kind of guy who could become withdrawn, negative, and stubborn. I could get crazy about defending some rule or regulation that has nothing to do with the problem, etc.*

> *The big signal that I'm operating defectively is when I hear myself say, "I don't care."*

Let's use the continuum to check where we are and where we are headed under stressful situations. Again, try to identify which characteristic is driving you and to what extent. Place a check on the continuum and where you feel you are. Mark your primary style and the style you move to under stressful conditions.

Emotional Responses to the World

VICE   **VIRTUE**

Lust--- Innocence

Sloth---Action

Anger---Serenity

Pride-- Humility

Deceit -- Truthfulness

Envy -- Equanimity

Greed --   ------------------------- Detachment

Fear-- Courage

Gluttony---Sobriety

Cognitive/Intellectual Responses to the World

VICE   **VIRTUE**

Vindication --- Justice

Resignation --Love

Perfection -- Wholeness

Co-Dependence --Freedom

Efficiency--Hope

Specialness--Originality

Intellectualization --- Understanding

Doubt/Dogma --Faith

Pleasure-- Work

Authenticity

FEAR	CORE SELF
Weakness	Power
Conflict	Peace
Anger	Goodness
Needy	Love
Failure	Efficiency
Ordinariness	Originality
Emptiness	Wisdom
Deviance	Loyalty
Pain	Joy

Go back and revisit these from time to time to see if you notice a *trend* upwards over time. Feel free to evaluate where you are according to all the number styles.

Finally, in this chapter, we'd like to formulate a profile of where we go under relaxed conditions. Review chapter 4 in this workbook. Write down the positive ways you think, speak, and act under relaxed conditions. Add to that all the positive traits you notice when you are relaxed.

> *I am extremely productive and efficient. I can plan projects and get them done quickly and efficiently. I'm reliable and can make fair decisions.*

In the chapter that describes your primary style in Wagner's book, locate the section titled, "A shift to the Low Side of Style *3* ." Read that paragraph. List what seems to fit you.

> *I can engage in busy work, etc.*
> *I can assume a role and forget who I am.*

If you want more information, find the chapter that is dedicated to the style number you go to under relaxed conditions. Read through the negative descriptors, and go through the negative portions of that particular style; area of avoidance, defense mechanism, vice, distorted core characteristics, distorting paradigm, and passion. Form a profile of how you could respond to situations under relaxed conditions in a negative way. I'm sure you have noticed other destructive ways you act under relaxed conditions. List those as well.

I can become critical and ignore my own feelings.
I am sometimes embarrassed by my feelings and
become heady, intellectual, etc.

Let's use the continuum to check where we are and where we are headed under relaxed conditions. Place a check on the continuum where you think you are presently. Which characteristic seems to be motivating you and to what extent is it driving your behavior? Mark your primary style and the style you move to under relaxed conditions. Again, feel free to evaluate yourself on all the styles.

Emotional Responses to the World

VICE   **VIRTUE**

Lust-- Innocence

Sloth--Action

Anger--Serenity

Pride-- Humility

Deceit --- Truthfulness

Envy --- Equanimity

Greed --- Detachment

Fear --- Courage

Gluttony--Sobriety

Cognitive/Intellectual Responses to the World

VICE	VIRTUE
Vindication	Justice
Resignation	Love
Perfection	Wholeness
Co-Dependence	Freedom
Efficiency	Hope
Specialness	Originality
Intellectualization	Understanding
Doubt/Dogma	Faith
Pleasure	Work

Authenticity

FEAR   **CORE SELF**

Weakness--Power

Conflict---Peace

Anger-- Goodness

Needy --Love

Failure --- Efficiency

Ordinariness --Originality

Emptiness ---Wisdom

Deviance--- Loyalty

Pain --- Joy

Again, go back and revisit these from time to time to see if you notice a *trend* upwards over time.

Here is what is important about this chapter. Good things happen to us every day and bad things happen to us every day. There will be things that happen to us during the course of everyday life. Other things will catch us when we are going through a stressful period of time. Further, there will be many things that come our way when we are relaxed. It's important for us to profile ourselves so we can respond in resourceful ways. If we know what our weaknesses are, we can hopefully be able to say, "My profile is this. I can see the temptation to respond to this in some very non-resourceful ways. However, I can choose to respond in more healthy and resourceful ways."

This requires some serious and brutally honest self-examination. That's what we have tried to accomplish in this chapter. Oh, I should probably tell you, there is more of this throughout the rest of the workbook.

REFLECTIONS

1. What have I learned new about myself?

2. What do I like about what I've learned about myself?

3. What do I need to revisit and/or follow up on?

4. What can I bring to my spiritual director or counselor
for further discussion?

Chapter 8

TOO MUCH OF A GOOD THING

My wife and I like to stay at Spanish run resorts on the ocean in Playa Del Carmen, Mexico. Earlier in the day, my wife often stopped at a French crepe stand on the resort. They would make a crepe and then fill it with your favorite ice cream.

One evening at dinner, we were at the place where we were both on the top end of feeling full and satisfied. You know that feeling; when you know you are full; and one more bite would push you over the line into feeling uncomfortable. I think we both crossed the line. I had an extra glass of wine and my wife had one more piece of fruit. Needless to say, we decided to take a walk after dinner to walk it off.

During our walk, we happened to pass the French crepe stand. My wife said, "John, you have to have one of these crepes. They are unbelievable." Me, being weak minded said, "Sure, let's try one." We each ordered a crepe stuffed with ice cream. Keep in mind, we were already overfilled. Even though we felt more uncomfortable with each bite; we kept eating because they tasted so good. At this point, we were actually sick and it was hard to walk back to the room where we crashed on the bed like snakes that swallowed whole cows; waiting for the food to digest.

Every bite of food we ate that night was superb and every drink was perfect. The problem is that even too much of a good thing can be bad for you.

That's kind of what describes our idealized selves. On page 7 of Wagner's book, the chart lists, from the inner circle out; our Authentic Values, our Area of Avoidance, or Defense Mechanisms and our Idealized Self-Image.

For now, just look at how our core values are distorted:

Authentic Core Value	Idealized Self-Image
Power	I am powerful
Peace	I am settled
Goodness	I am right
Love	I am helpful
Efficacy	I am successful
Originality	I am special
Wisdom	I am perceptive
Loyalty	I am obedient
Joy	I am okay

I'm sure you have noticed how similar these two lists are. That is exactly what the danger is. It's like that with counterfeit money as well. The better the counterfeit; the more danger there is that they will go undetected and, ultimately, destroy the value of our authentic economy.

In the last chapter, we explored some of the non-resourceful ways we respond to people and events we encounter. Hopefully, you have identified how you use these non-resourceful tactics in different kinds of situations. Part of the goal in this workbook is to help us identify these non-resourceful behaviors and then replace them with resourceful behaviors. This is easier said than done.

Let's review how we form these false Self-Images.

List what your area of avoidance is, along with some other major fears you have.

Conflict / Pain / Abandonment /
Being shunned and left out, etc.

We learn how to avoid these by building up defense mechanisms. These defense mechanisms take the form of thoughts, words, and actions. They can also take the form of non-thinking, silence, and inaction. In the last chapter, we looked at these and profiled ourselves.

Can you see how these non-resourceful tactics help steer us away from and around our fears and areas of avoidance? We have done this for so long that they become our natural way of being. It's like athletes who practice specific moves; a baseball swing, a tennis stroke, a particular dive, etc. They do it so often, they no longer think about it. This is called muscle memory.

In Wagner's book, take time to go to both chapters that describe your primary style and your wing style, and read the section labeled "How the Distortion of This Style Developed." Take time to pray and meditate as you read these sections. Christians ought to ask for the guidance and consolation of the Holy Spirit as they examine these. This exercise is more likely to be painful than not. All of these may apply, some of these may apply, or you may have other experiences that you remember having shaped you. Write down your observations.

I felt alone and left out.
I thought I had to earn people's love, etc.

Go back and review from chapter 7 in the workbook how you responded to these situations with non-resourceful tactics. Then write down the statement from page 7 in Wagner's workbook what you say about yourself as the Idealized self. Also, try to describe what this statement means in depth.

"I am settled. I am okay." – I am really laid back and
don't let things bother me. I'm fine, etc.

Can you see how you got to this Idealized Self-Image? Take some time to think about what you do to get to the essence of these statements. What do you have to deny or deceive yourself about to get there?

The big lie I tell myself is, "I don't care."
The problem with this lie is that it "works".
If I can't have something or am denied something,
I move quickly to, "It doesn't matter. I don't need it.
It's not that important to me, etc."

Don't go on until you can identify how much time, energy, and money you put into living these Idealized Self-Images. If we are going to become very resourceful human beings; we must first acknowledge and own our non-resourceful behaviors. Make sure you can recognize the difference between the Authentic Value and the Idealized Self-Image. Jews and Christians can set up the contrast by putting the adjective "godly" before the Authentic Value and "counterfeit" before that Authentic Value to describe the Idealized Self-Image.

For example, let's take a 9. The Authentic Value is peace. The Idealized Self-Image is "I am settled." These sound similar but in reality they couldn't be further apart.

The Hebrew word for peace is *shalom*. It never means the absence of conflict. In fact, the Psalms are full of situations filled with pain and conflict while at the same time claiming the peace of God. For the Hebrew, peace means being in a right relationship with God; no matter what the circumstances are. Peace can mean that all is well with my soul through painful situations, and even through the valley of the shadow of death.

On the other hand, "I am settled" can mean that nothing is encroaching on my circle of comfort. If something is approaching that will cause conflict or pain, I will just ignore it or avoid it. I can say that these people don't matter to me when they hurt me. I can emotionally write them off. Just as long as there is nothing in my face, "I am settled." It takes a great deal of ignoring reality to get to this state.

In order to experience true peace, one must embrace the pain and find the presence and comfort of God in the midst of it. It is truly the ability to say, "All is well with my soul" in the very depths of the pain and conflict.

"It is well with my soul" is a Christian hymn written by Horatio G. Spafford. The story is an interesting one that confronts this counterfeit idea of "I am settled" and embraces the true peace of God. During the 1860's, Spafford lived on the north side of Chicago with his wife, Anna, and their five children. He was wealthy and had a lot of money tied up in real estate on the lakefront in Chicago. They were godly people who supported many missionaries and evangelists like D. L. Moody. They had it all.

Then, their 4-year-old son caught Scarlet Fever and died. Shortly after, came the Chicago fire that burned up most of Spafford's holdings. Thinking they would take a break before restarting all their businesses, Spafford and his wife decided to take their four daughters for some time of recovery in France. Part of the reason was that Anna's health started to deteriorate and this restful stay in France may help. They had their tickets and it came time to board the ship. Spafford got an urgent business call and not wanting to disappoint the children, sent his wife and daughters on ahead. He would catch the next ship. In the middle of the Atlantic Ocean, an iron ship collided with the passenger ship that carried Spafford's wife and daughters. It took only twelve minutes for the ship to sink. Anna was picked up from the debris and then put on an American ship in the area. She was taken to a hospital in Wales. From there she sent her husband this tragic message, "Saved alone. What shall I do?" Horatio left as soon as he got the message that his four daughters had drowned. As he crossed the Atlantic, the captain of the ship called him to the deck and informed him that as close as he could calculate, this was the spot his daughters drowned in the accident.

That night in his cabin, he penned the song, "It is Well With My Soul." Here are the words:

> When peace, like a river, attendeth my way,
> When sorrows like sea billows roll;
> Whatever my lot, Thou has taught me to say,
> It is well, it is well, with my soul.
>
> (refrain) It is well, with my soul,
> It is well, with my soul,
> It is well, it is well, with my soul.
>
> Though Satan should buffet, though trials should come,
> Let this blest assurance control,
> That Christ has regarded my helpless estate,
> And hath shed His own blood for my soul.
>
> (refrain)
>
> My sin, oh, the bliss of this glorious thought!
> My sin, not in part but the whole,
> Is nailed to the cross, and I bear it no more,
> Praise the Lord, praise the Lord, O my soul!
>
> (refrain)

And Lord, haste the day when my faith shall be sight,
The clouds be rolled back as a scroll;
The trump shall resound, and the Lord shall descend,
Even so, it is well with my soul.

(refrain)

The defective way of describing peace is to describe it as the absence of pain and conflict; hence, directing us to maintain the Idealized Self-Image of "I am settled." That is exactly the opposite of peace defined as an Authentic Value.

At this point, try and define the difference between your Authentic Value and the defective way of manifesting itself as your Idealized Self-Image.

I have exchanged genuine peace for the cheap substitute, "I am settled. I'm okay." My version of peace is an insult to the biblical definition of peace.

It is believed that the first step to recovery is admitting I have a problem. In our case we'll call this owning up to who we are. In Wagner's book, these two exercises are called "Me and Not-Me," and "Re-owning the Not-Me." Carefully read those two exercises, found on pages 11 and 12 of his book.

I want to emphasize that the characteristics we most dislike in others are usually weaknesses in our own lives.

Me and Not-me

Me	Not-Me
Kind	*Mean*
Generous	*Stingy*
Peaceful	*Argumentative*
Joyful	*Depressing*
Positive	*Negative*
Hard working	*Lazy*
Dependable	*Irresponsible*
Team Player	*Self-centered*

Me	Not-Me

Re-owning the Not-Me (It helps to take each Not-Me characteristic and preface it with the phrase, "I can sometimes be." For example, "I can sometimes be mean." Take time to define specific instances when you have been mean. Do that with each Not-Me characteristic.

I can be mean sometimes when someone has treated
me badly or if I feel I was treated unfairly.

I can be stingy if someone is always
freeloading off the rest of us.

I can be negative, self-centered, and lazy,
if things are not going well.

If you are having trouble with this exercise, go to page 12 in Wagner's book and try to get at this idea by working through the section "Reframing the Not-Me."

It's important for us to own this Shadow Side (Jung's term) of our personality because it is a part of us that we hide in order to maintain our counterfeit selves (Idealized Self-Image.) One of the great benefits of embracing our shadow side is that it exposes our Idealized Self-Image as false.

You may have to sit with this chapter for several weeks or even months until you own up to the counterfeit self you have built, embracing the characteristics of your shadow side, and then making the following statement:

Even though I am _(Idealized Self-Image Statement)_ does not mean I am experiencing genuine _(Authentic Value)_.

Even though I am settled; this does not mean I am experiencing genuine peace.

Take some time to meditate and journal about your thoughts in regards to this powerful statement you have just made. In the next couple of chapters, we will attempt to deconstruct these non-resourceful ways of being.

Journal

I have spent over 60 years building up this counterfeit self. I have convinced myself that genuine peace is simply the absence of conflict.

I know I escape through watching television, eating, drinking, etc.

*The journey will be difficult for me because the
counterfeit is seemingly so close to the real thing.
For example: am I being polite, kind, engaging, etc.
because these are genuine acts of kindness;
or am I simply avoiding conflict?*

*I can see the counterfeit is harming me physically,
spiritually, and emotionally.*

REFLECTIONS

1. What have I learned new about myself?

2. What do I like about what I've learned about myself?

3. What do I need to revisit and/or follow up on?

4. What can I bring to my spiritual director or counselor
for further discussion?

Chapter 9

CLEANING UP YOUR VISION

We have all had the experience of going to the eye doctor for a vision check-up. As you look through the refracting machine, the doctor will say, "Is A better," then switch the lens and say, "or is B better?" She will do this several times, switching the lens and saying, "Is A better or B better? Is C better or D better?" She is making sure that the images you see are as clear as possible.

In Wagner's book, *Nine Lenses on the World*, he uses Jeffrey Young's description of how the "lenses" we view life through can be distorted and, therefore, give us false interpretations. For our purposes, that description seems to be helpful.

Events approach us and enter into our individual world. These events are processed through our lenses. Based on our processing of these events, we make interpretations concerning the meaning of each event. Like our physical eyesight, the "correct" interpretation depends on how clear and how sharp our lenses are. If our lenses are distorted, then we will make false interpretations and come to wrong conclusions. For example, if we were to look at an anorexic objectively, we would tell them they are seriously underweight. However, through their distorted lenses, they would think of themselves as fat.

Our goal is to become more authentic by looking at the events coming to us through lenses of the core values laid out by the Enneagram. For Christians, the language could be that we want to take in and interpret events through the fruit of the Holy Spirit Who indwells us.

Let's try to look at this with the metaphor of a lens:

			Interpretation of
	>	>	
Events coming our way	> Lens	>	events that
	>	>	influence our response.

We want to focus on the Lens portion. Let's focus on the things that distort our lenses. Think about it this way. Events are coming at us. The objective data has to somehow make through all the distortions if we are going to come up with a right interpretation. The lens area in a distorted lens is like the old video game "Frogger." In the game, a frog tries to cross a busy highway. Unless you are really skilled, your frog is often hit by a car. That's how difficult it is for an objective event to get to you untainted. Now look at some of the things that are distorting your lens.

The primary distortion in this area is our "Idealized Self-Image." In the last chapter, you wrote down the statement that described your Idealized self-image and then how the statement described a lot of your behavior. Take time to write down your Idealized self-image along with how that causes you to interpret events in distorted ways. Be as specific as you can.

I am settled. I am okay. When I have been hurt by someone or something, I tell myself, "I'm okay. What happened wasn't so bad and it really didn't hurt me or affect me." I bury the hurt to the point I really don't feel it.

I have had no way to experience sadness, grief, disappointment, etc.

Combine this with your area of avoidance and other fears.

I avoid conflict. I also deal with the fear of being inadequate in situations and of being abandoned or left behind.

Think of a particular situation in which you reacted based on avoidance, fear, and/or your idealized self-image.

I had grown to love and trust some people,
who later betrayed me and said some very harmful
and hurtful things about me; all of which were not true.
They further spread these lies.

1. *I said things like, "I don't care. It doesn't matter. I'll be okay. It's no big deal."*

2. *I never let the full hurt of all that sink deep in my heart and soul.*

3. *I did the religious thing and just prayed for forgiveness for them.*

This distortion came from fear; fear of pain,
fear of rejection, fear of being inadequate to
face the problems, etc.

As you look back on those events, can you take off these distorted lenses and acknowledge the events for what they were?

For no reason at all, these people betrayed me and hurt me deeply. I had given them my time, money, and energy. I sacrificed for them. What they did was hurtful. They proved to be untrustworthy people.

Oftentimes, we may have the insight but not the ability to let go of these distortions. If that's the case, go back to Chapter 5 in this workbook and see which of your positive strengths you can use to clean up these distortions.

I'm honest. I'm strong. I'm loyal. I'm a good worker. I have survived hurts in the past. I can survive present and future hurts. I can face the conflict, work through it, and truly be at peace.

Work at this continually. Perhaps you want to write stick-up notes with your authentic core value on them. Put them on your mirror, keep one in the car, put them in your notebooks, and keep them at work. Continue to affirm who you are. As you process past events, present events, and prepare for future events, follow the next steps:

1. As you observe a particular event, note your knee-jerk reaction.

2. Name your distortions, avoidances, and fears.

3. Use your resources from Chapter 5 to counteract these.

4. Analyze the events according to your corrected vision.

5. Meditate on and take time to formulate your response to the event.

6. Evaluate yourself; being brutally honest.

7. If you "failed," work out a plan to succeed in the future.

8. Make sure to note and rejoice in your successes. Honestly facing our failures is a success also.

Remember, we have dealt with only one or two instances. Don't downplay that. You can take this and apply the principles as you continue on.

I want to emphasize this point. The way to your authentic core self necessarily has to journey back through your areas of avoidance and fears. To become healthy, we need to embrace those things we have been avoiding. You now know you have to use tools to get to your core self.

Let's use another evaluation tool that we learned about in Chapter 7 of this workbook. As you analyze how you received the event, interpreted the event, and reacted to the event; analyze whether you were moving towards your virtue or vice. If you need to, go back and review your answers for Chapter 7 of the workbook.

Which way are you moving?

Emotional Responses to the World

VICE   **VIRTUE**

Lust-- Innocence

Sloth---Action

Anger---Serenity

Pride--- Humility

Deceit-- ---------------------------- Truthfulness

Envy --- Equanimity

Greed--- -------------------Detachment

Fear-- Courage

Gluttony---Sobriety

Cognitive/Intellectual Responses to the World

VICE   **VIRTUE**

Vindication -- Justice

Resignation --Love

Perfection -- Wholeness

Co-Dependence ---Freedom

Efficiency---Hope

Specialness-- Originality

Intellectualization -- Understanding

Doubt/Dogma --Faith

Pleasure-- Work

Authenticity

FEAR	CORE SELF
Weakness	Power
Conflict	Peace
Anger	Goodness
Needy	Love
Failure	Efficiency
Ordinariness	Originality
Emptiness	Wisdom
Deviance	Loyalty
Pain	Joy

Are you starting to move away from the vice towards the virtue?

Yes I am.

REFLECTIONS

1. What have I learned new about myself?

2. What do I like about what I've learned about myself?

3. What do I need to revisit and/or follow up on?

4. What can I bring to my spiritual director or counselor
for further discussion?

Chapter 10

PUT IT DOWN IN WRITING

By now, you should know where your weaknesses lie, what kinds of situations you are most likely to misinterpret, the kinds of non-resourceful behaviors that you slip into, and the resources to correct all of these. It's one thing to acknowledge these things intellectually; but quite another to actually write them down, analyze them, and make a plan to change them.

In this chapter, I would like you to journal for about a month. If you like this practice of journaling and you find you are growing from it, then make it part of your daily practice. I have included a sample of what your journal could look like; feel free to copy those pages and complete them as your personal journal.

Up to this point, I have fought the temptation to bring Christian principles into this workbook. However, I want to share my belief that people can change and since our lives have purpose, we should work to replace our non-resourceful thoughts, words, and behaviors with resourceful ones.

If you are not Christian, I encourage you to look at these from your religious perspective or a humanistic perspective.

Each person is uniquely created by God:

Psalms 139:13-16 (TNIV)

"¹³For you created my inmost being;
*   you knit me together in my mother's womb.*

> *¹⁴I praise you because I am fearfully and wonderfully made;*
> *your works are wonderful,*
> *I know that full well.*
>
> *¹⁵My frame was not hidden from you*
> *when I was made in the secret place.*
> *When I was woven together in the depths of the earth,*
>
> *¹⁶your eyes saw my unformed body.*
> *All the days ordained for me*
> *were written in your book*
> *before one of them came to be."*

We were no mistake. We were no accident. God created each one of us. He gave each one a particular personality and individual experiences that have shaped us into unique individuals.

Since we have been handcrafted by God, we each have a purpose and a destiny to fulfill:

Ephesians 2:10 (NLT)

> *"¹⁰For we are God's masterpiece. He has created us anew in Christ Jesus, so we can do the good things he planned for us long ago."*

We have all been created to be unique; one of a kind. We have different genetic codes and we have each gone through a unique set of experiences. In this verse, we see that we are God's masterpiece. It doesn't matter what our Enneagram type is or how horrific a life we have led; God can use our particular personalities and experiences to help others. My hope is that working through the Enneagram and this workbook might help you see the masterpiece you are; and are in the process of becoming.

Growing and Maturing are difficult processes. We may be tempted to quit:

1 Corinthians 10:13 (NLT)

"¹³The temptations in your life are no different from what others experience. And God is faithful. He will not allow the temptation to be more than you can stand. When you are tempted, He will show you a way out so that you can endure."

Almost anything in life worth achieving is difficult and takes a great deal of hard work, patience, courage, and humility. Growing into the men and women God has destined us to be is hard work. Many people find it too difficult and give up. My hunch is that if you have made it this far in the workbook, you are serious about becoming a healthy and resourceful human being. Other people have taken this journey and succeeded. There is no reason to think you can't.

We have extra help; supernatural help:

John 15:5 (NLT)

⁵Yes, I am the vine; you are the branches. Those who remain in me, and I in them, will produce much fruit. For apart from me you can do nothing."

Jesus made it clear to His followers that if we depend solely on our human strengths, talents, and abilities; we will never be able to reach these lofty goals. However, He just as clearly made it known that He is willing to live in us and journey through life with us. In fact, He promised to empower us to become the men and women He wants us to be.

With God all things are possible:

Philippians 4:13 (NLT)

"¹³For I can do everything through Christ, who gives me strength."

The wonderful truth is that Jesus doesn't expect us to be able to complete life on our own. We can do all things when we submit to the power of God. We can become healthy, productive, and happy human beings.

God gives us the desire to do good and then empowers us to do it:

Philippians 2:13 (NLT)

"13For God is working in you, giving you the desire and the power to do what pleases him."

God actually puts the desire in us to grow and mature as believers. If you are working through this workbook, the chances are that God put the desire in you to grow. That is amazing in itself. However, God promised that not only did He place the desire in us to grow; He will empower us to grow.

With these encouragements, take to the journaling task. Be brutally honest with yourself. Be humble, courageous, and live in grace during this process.

Christians will recognize this journal exercise to be very close to the prayer exercise of "Examen."

People of prayer should open the exercise with prayer and conclude the exercise with prayer.

Daily Journal

_____

(Date)

Review your day (If you are a Christian, do this under the guidance and the direction of the Holy Spirit). As you examine the day, what event or events seem to stand out? If there is more than one that stands out, do each one separately. Name the event(s).

Event #1 _____

Event #2 _____

Event #3 _____

Take time to replay the event in your mind. Do not judge it; merely try to recall it. Write down the details of the event as best as you can remember. Be sure to include:

1. The events leading up to the event.

2. The words spoken by you and others (as close to the exact words as you can get).

3. The feelings and thoughts going on inside of you as well as what you were physically feeling.

4. Describe the event in as much detail as you can.

Event #1:

A.

B.

C.

D.

Event #2:

A.

B.

C.

D.

Event #3:

A.

B.

C.

D.

Which center were you operating from (Head, heart, or gut)? _____ (Refer back to Chapter 6 in the workbook and pages 30-36 in Wagner's book, if you need to refresh your memory)

Based on the event(s), was that the best center to operate from? If not, which center would have been more helpful? How?

Event #1:

Event #2:

Event #3:

Which style were you operating under? _____

If you were in your "normal" style, were you exhibiting the resourceful or non-resourceful characteristics? List them.

How did your wing influence your response to the event?

Event #1:

Event #2:

Event #3:

If you were operating from your style under stressful conditions, comment on that.

Event #1:

Event #2:

Event #3:

If you were operating from your style under relaxed conditions, comment on that.

Event #1:

Event #2:

Event #3:

At the time of the event, did you identify your potential knee-jerk responses that may have led you to non-resourceful behavior? What were they?

Event #1:

Event #2:

Event #3:

Were you able to take all your positive qualities, apply them to the situation, and overcome your potentially non-resourceful behavior?

Event #1:

Event #2:

Event #3:

If so, how can you build on this in the future?

If you were not quite successful, go back and see some of the tools you have and see which ones of them you could have used.

Make a plan as to how you can overcome your non-resourceful behaviors.

After you are finished writing, go back and prayerfully or reflectively read what you wrote. Then, sit in silence and meditate on what words or thoughts come to you. Simply sit with them for a while.

REFLECTIONS

1. What have I learned new about myself?

2. What do I like about what I've learned about myself?

3. What do I need to revisit and/or follow up on?

4. What can I bring to my spiritual director or counselor
for further discussion?

Chapter 11

PLANNING THE WORK AND WORKING THE PLAN

There is a big difference between the statements and attitudes of, "I'd like to…" and "I'm going to…." I'd like to lose weight. Unfortunately, I pastor a church near one of the most famous bakeries in Chicago; the Swedish Bakery. One day while driving to church, I prayed, "Lord if it's Your will that I stop at the bakery, please find me a parking spot," and wouldn't you know it, there it was, an open spot right in front of the bakery … after only five times circling around the block! Obviously I'm still overweight because when I say, "I'd like to lose weight," that doesn't take any effort at all. When I get to the point where I say, "I'm going to lose weight," that takes commitment, a plan, and a lot of hard work.

As you have progressed through this workbook, have you identified anything you are ready to say at this point, "I'm going to …?" If you are working through this workbook and have made it this far, I'm sure you have identified some areas in which you are determined to move towards more resourceful behaviors.

I'm a big fan of Kaizen in the way we are encouraged to make small changes that are doable and then build on our successes little by little. Let's make a plan, remembering to use all the resources we have identified and that are available to us.

Step I – Identify one or two goals you would like to accomplish. Write them down. Remember to write them down with the formula, "I'm going to…"

I'm going to conquer gluttony

I'm going to conquer sloth

*I'm going to conquer talking as a way
to cover up my fear.*

As you look at these goals, if you're anything like me, they are pretty broad, kind of nebulous, and really hard to measure in terms of day to day, week to week progress.

Take each goal and write down specific instances that seem to contribute to blocking you from achieving this goal. For example, if you overeat, what are the specific instances that you most likely catch yourself overeating (i.e. when you are stressed, sad, depressed, nervous, etc.)?

*Gluttony – When I'm at home watching television,
I overeat.*

*Sloth – After work, when I'm tired,
I want a lot of mindless television.*

Talking – I talk a lot when I'm nervous.

Look at those hindrances and make some observations.

*Talking too much and overeating
are related to my mouth.*

Sloth and Gluttony work together and feed each other.

Planning the Work

The philosophy of this is to make some small goals and then throw all our strengths and resources at them. Hopefully, our strengths and resources will be so great and overwhelming compared to the task, we can most likely reach these goals and continue to build on them.

In setting some specific goals, make sure they are:

Measurable – In other words, make them specific enough that you can measure both progress and regress. For example, "I'm not going to over-eat today," is very difficult to measure. However, if you were to say, "I'm going to eat 1500 calories today," you can write down everything you eat and calculate the calories. If you ate 1500 calories, you met your goal for the day. If you ate over 1500 calories, you did not meet your goal. If you are trying to be a better husband, that is a noble goal but not very measurable. However, if you set your goal to give your wife one compliment a day, wash the dishes 3 times in the week, and buy her a small gift once a week; those are very objective and measurable. Set a goal that is objectively measurable. Not reaching the goal is not the same as failure. I believe it's not how many times we get knocked down that determines success; rather how many times we get up.

Doable – If we were to look at where we find ourselves now; remember it took us a lifetime to get here. We are not going to solve the problem in a day, a week, a month, or perhaps even a year. The point is that we move towards more resourceful behavior. For example, for a person who wants to start exercising, it would be unrealistic to set the goal of working out every day for two hours per day. I don't want to seem negative or rain on anyone's parade; but that's not going to happen. You may want to start out by working out for 3 times a week for 20 minutes per session. Every year, for the past 30 years, I have seen an influx of people come to the health club to work out every January. The club is crowded; but by the middle of

February, almost all of those people have given up or died, and the club returns to normal. I would prefer that none of you die or give up.

Identifying other strengths – Oftentimes, we have resources available to us that we don't think about. For example, someone trying to drink less may want to attend Alcoholics Anonymous. Oftentimes, we forget our spiritual resources. Again, you will have to draw on your own particular religious or humanistic tradition. Christians have the Spiritual Disciplines to help them. Some of these are prayer, Bible study, Lectio Divina, fasting, serving, giving, meditating, journaling, solitude, silence, just to name a few. We have supernatural resources available to us. Christians can depend on God, the Holy Spirit, to inspire and empower them. Further, you will notice that the fruit of the Holy Spirit is extremely close to the desired traits in the Enneagram. The fruit of the Spirit is: love, joy, peace, patience, kindness, goodness, faithfulness, gentleness, and self-control. And, let's not forget to incorporate our human resources: family, friends, counselors, spiritual directors, mentors, etc. The more resources we bring to bear on our goals; the more chance we have to succeed.

Write Out Your Goals (Explain how they are helping you.)

Goal #1 Exercise – I will work out at night when possible. It will help me lose weight. I will get healthy and the healthier I get, the more I will want to lose weight. It will help me to wind down after work and I'll have less time to watch television and eat.

Goal #2 Silence – At least once per day,
after exchanging pleasantries, I will not speak to the
other person for at least 5 minutes unless
he/she speaks directly to me.

Working The Plan

- Make three or four copies of these goals and post them in places you will see them throughout the day. For example, place a copy where you are sure to see it when you get up in the morning, by your computer at home, by your television, at your work desk, in your car, wherever you will be reminded of these goals throughout the day.

- Design an evaluation sheet by which you can mark down and evaluate how you have done during the day. The evaluation should contain the goal (it can simply be written as Goal #1, Goal #2, etc), a space where you can write "yes or no" depending on whether or not you achieved the goal, and a section for comment where you can make notes to yourself as to what contributed to achieving or missing your goal. The following is an example.

- If you have a counselor, Spiritual Director, mentor, or good friend, it's best to share your progress or regress with them.

- Stay with each goal until you accomplish it. If you find it doesn't quite fit or accomplish what you want to accomplish, feel free to tweak it.

- When you accomplish a goal, up the ante a little and set a little higher goal for yourself.

Keep in mind that growth is a lifelong process. Be patient with yourself and continue to grow.

Goal	Achieved		Observations
Goal #1	Yes		I planned to meet a workout partner at the club today.

REFLECTIONS

1. What have I learned new about myself?

2. What do I like about what I've learned about myself?

3. What do I need to revisit and/or follow up on?

4. What can I bring to my spiritual director or counselor for further discussion? Periodically, I will do a formal check-up to measure my progress.

Chapter 12

WHERE DO WE GO FROM HERE?

You have put a lot of hard work into becoming a more resourceful person. You have become very aware of your strengths and weaknesses. By now, you know how to make plans to turn your weaknesses into strengths by using the tools in your emotional toolbox.

At this point, I think it is worth revisiting what we have said from the beginning; that since we are complex persons, it would be a good idea to draw from the strengths of other personality styles.

For example, it is desirable for us to incorporate all these into our personalities:

The goodness of style 1

The love of style 2

The efficacy of style 3

The originality of style 4

The wisdom of style 5

The loyalty of style 6

The joy of style 7

The power of style 8

The peace of style 9

Here is the plan I am suggesting. Work through the workbook again as if you were each of these styles. Of course, you could pick a style randomly or you could work through the styles in numerical order (1-9).

However, I would like to work at it through a different approach. We have been working through this process developing tools and perfecting our skill in using them. Therefore, I would like to work with what we are most familiar with and work steadily to what we are least familiar with.

Formulating an Order for Further Study

Note: This paradigm works perfectly for styles 1, 3, 6, 8, and 9. For styles 2, 4, 5, and 7, work through the exercise as outlined below. However, if you come across a style you have already gone through, skip it, and then go on with the exercises. When you are finished, then go back and do the styles that you have not covered.

1. Now that you have worked through your primary style, work through your dominate wing. In other words, if you are a 9 with a 1 wing, work through the workbook as if style 1 were your primary style.

2. After you have done a complete study as if your wing were your primary style, move to your less dominate wing. In other words, if you are a style 9 with a 1 wing, your next study will be to adapt the 8 as your primary style. Work your way through the workbook as if you were an 8.

3. Next, move to the style you go to under relaxed conditions and adapt that as your primary style. For example, if you are a 9, you move to 3 under relaxed conditions. Work through the book as if your primary style was 3.

4. Look at the analysis sheet you received when you took the WEPSS. Look at the two wings that surround the style you just worked through. For the 9 who goes to 3 under relaxed conditions, styles 2 & 4 are the wings. On the last page of the WEPSS analysis, look at the chart listed "Percentile Scores and find out which of those two styles you scored higher in. Further identify as to which style you were most resourceful in. Resourceful takes precedence. Work through that style next. In other words, between style 2 and style 4, which were you the highest and most resourceful in? Work through the workbook as if you were that particular style.

5. Then, go to the other wing. For example, if you worked through style 2, now work through the workbook as if style 4 was your primary style.

6. Next, identify the style you normally go to under stressful conditions. A 9 goes to 6 under stressful conditions. Work through the workbook as if your primary style was a 6.

7. Identify the wings on either side of this style. In our scenario, styles 5 & 7 are the wings. On the last page of the WEPSS analysis, look at the chart listed "Percentile Scores and find out which of those two styles you scored higher in. Further, identify which style you were most resourceful in. Remember, Resourceful takes precedence. Work through that style next. In other words, between style 5 and style 7, which were you the highest and most resourceful in? Work through the workbook as if you were that particular style.

8. Then, go to the other wing. For example, if you worked through style 5, now work through the workbook as if style 7 was your primary style.

9. If your primary style is 1, 3, 6, 8, or 9, you have now worked through all the styles. If you are a 2, 4, 5, or 7, work through the remaining styles. This means you have worked through the workbook nine times. You should now be extremely familiar with the Enneagram and how it works in your life.

Remember, our goal is to become the most complete and resourceful human beings we can.

For believers, we are invited to take these and all the fruit of the Spirit to manifest itself in us; love, joy, peace, patience, kindness, goodness, gentleness, faithfulness, and self-control.

This is a lifelong process. Good luck!

CPSIA information can be obtained
at www.ICGtesting.com
Printed in the USA
BVHW052108110819
555539BV00005B/92/P